A DORLING KINDERSLEY BOOK

Editor Dawn Sirett
Managing Editor Jane Yorke
Designer Karen Fielding
Art Editor Jane Coney
Senior Art Editor Mark Richards
Production Jayne Wood

Photography by Steve Shott
Additional photography by Jane Burton
(ginger kitten page 6 and grey kitten page 7)
and Dave King (pages 14-15)
Illustrations by Jane Cradock-Watson and Dave Hopkins
Animals supplied by Trevor Smith's Animal World,
Howletts Zoo Park, Intellectual Animals,
and A1 Animals

Eye Openers ®

First published in Great Britain in 1992
by Dorling Kindersley Limited,
9 Henrietta Street, London WC2E 8PS
Reprinted 1993, 1995
Copyright © 1992 Dorling Kindersley Limited, London

A CIP catalogue record for this book is available
from the British Library.

ISBN 0-86318-755-2

Reproduced by Colourscan, Singapore
Printed and bound in Italy by L.E.G.O., Vicenza

·EYE·OPENERS·

Baby Animals

Written by Angela Royston

DK

DORLING KINDERSLEY
London • New York • Stuttgart

Kitten

ear

When kittens are born, they cannot see or hear. They sleep a lot and suck milk from the mother cat. These playful kittens are eight weeks old. They can eat meat from dishes. They will soon go to a new home.

eye

fur

Duckling

Ducklings hatch from eggs. Soon after hatching, they follow the mother duck to the pond to find food. These ducklings are just one day old. In a few weeks they will lose their soft down and grow feathers.

head

beak

down

foot

9

Leopard cub

ear

This wild leopard cub is four months old. She likes to run and pounce with her brother and sister. The mother leopard watches over the cubs and brings them meat to eat. When the cubs are older, they will learn to hunt for themselves.

10

tail

leg

paw

Piglet

Piglets can stand up and
walk around as soon
as they are born. These
piglets were born on
a farm only three days
ago. They squeal loudly as
they feed on the mother
pig's milk. Soon
they will learn
to eat solid
food from
a trough.

mouth

snout   hoof   tail

13

Wallaby

This baby wallaby is four months old. He is carried around safely inside his mother's pouch. Sometimes he climbs out to explore. He hops along, looking for plants to eat.

tail

ear

foot

Puppy

ear

Puppies like to play together. Sometimes they pretend to fight. These puppies are eight weeks old and are big enough to leave their mother. Soon they will learn to walk on a lead like older dogs.

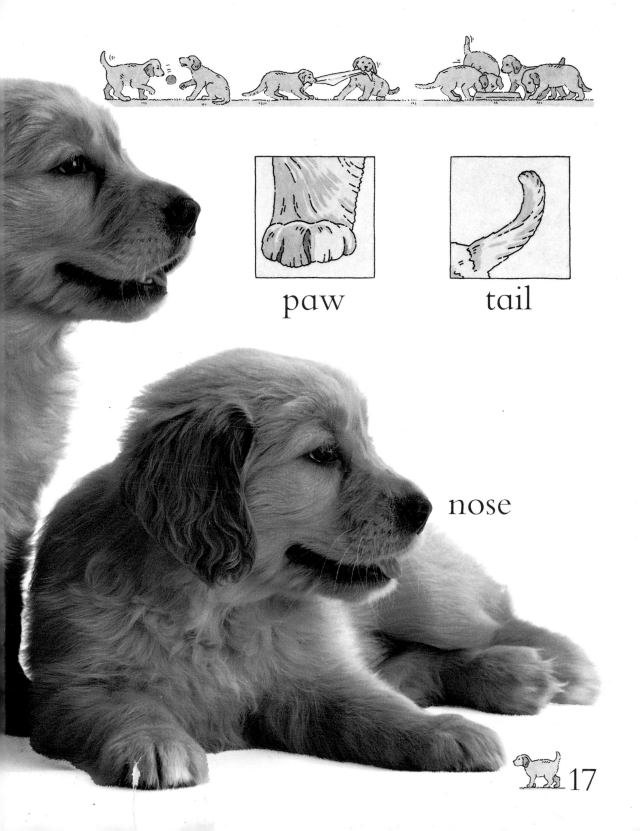

paw

tail

nose

17

Fawn

A fawn can stand up on its wobbly legs almost as soon as it is born. This shy fawn is ten weeks old. She still feeds on the mother deer's milk. When she is older, the fawn will eat leaves and grass.

ear

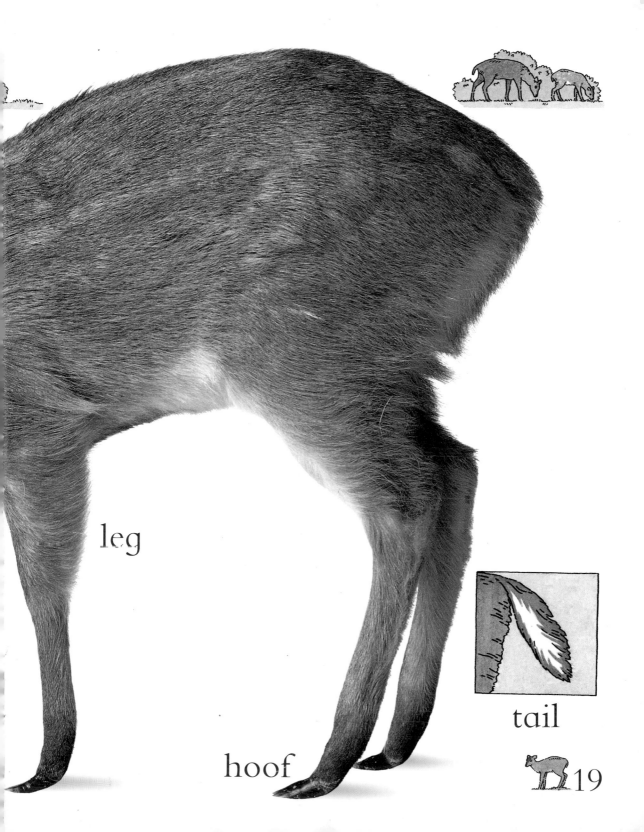

leg

hoof

tail

19

Gorilla

A baby gorilla is carried around by its mother and feeds on her milk. This baby gorilla is seven months old. He can walk on all fours and is beginning to eat leaves and fruit. Soon he will play with the other young gorillas in his tribe.

hand

foot

leg

21